The Deer and the Earwig
A Poem and a Story

I Hear with my Little Ear

I hear with my little ear. . .

Hooray! Hooray!
A very loud cheer.

I hear with my little ear. . .

A very loud **bump**!
(My dad can't steer.)

I hear with my little ear. . .

A snap of twigs.

It's a very shy deer.

The Deer and the Earwig

Here is a stream. Here is a deer.

And here is a little black earwig.

Oh dear! The earwig has fallen into the stream!
"Help! Help!" he cries.

"Do not fear, I am here," says the deer.
She drops a leaf into the stream.

The earwig climbs on to the leaf.
He sails to the bank.

"Thank you, deer," says the earwig.
"You saved my life."

A week later. . .
Here is the stream. Here is the deer.
And here is the little black earwig.

Oh dear! Here is a hunter!
He has a spear.

The deer can't see the hunter.
She can't hear him.

Help! The hunter lifts his spear.

But here comes the earwig.

"Do not fear, I am here!" he says.

The earwig nips the hunter's ear.
The hunter jumps and drops the spear.

The deer runs away.

"Thank you, earwig," says the deer.
"You saved my life."

Hare and Tortoise go to School

Lucy Floyd
Illustrated by Adria Meserve

Hare and Tortoise went
to school.
They had a race.

3

Tortoise went on the bus.
Hare ran down the road.

school

5

Hare ran up the hill.

Hare ran down the hill.

7

Hare ran into the park.

"I'm hungry," said Hare.

drinks
cakes
ice cream
sandwiches

10

He got some food.

The bus went down the road.

"Oh, no!" said Hare.

school bus

13

Hare ran fast.
At last, he got to school.

school

school bus

15

"You win!" said Hare.

Playtime Poems

Compiled by John Foster

Contents

Acknowledgements

The Editor and Publisher wish to thank the following who have kindly given permission for the use of copyright material:

Eric Finney for 'Playground problems' and 'Playground quarrel' both © 1995 Eric Finney; Julie Holder for 'Round and round' © 1995 Julie Holder; Richard James for 'Inside, outside' © 1995 Richard James; Tony Mitton for 'Tiger tag' © 1995 Tony Mitton; Brian Moses for 'Out-time, in-time' © 1995 Brian Moses; Irene Rawnsley for 'On the slide' © 1995 Irene Rawnsley; Jill Townsend for 'Conkers' © 1995 Jill Townsend.

Round and round

Round and round
On the roundabout
To and fro
On the swing
Up and down
On the see-saw
Bounce
On the trampoline spring

Up the ladder
Through the bars
Down the pole
Of the climbing frame
Up the ladder
And down the slide
Then do it all again.

Julie Holder

3

Out-time, in-time

Out-time, out-time,
run around and shout time,
shake it all about time,
out-time, out-time.

In-time, in-time,
it's time to begin time,
stop the noisy din time,
in-time, in-time.

Brian Moses

5

Tiger tag

Tiger tag! Tiger tag!
One, two, three!
Tiger tag! Tiger tag!
You can't catch me!

Harry got an elephant
just for a pet.
Harry took it home
in a jumbo jet.

6

Larry got a lion
and took it to the zoo.
Kerry got a tiger
and I've got YOU!

Tony Mitton

Playground problems

Please, Miss:
Kevin Jones has
burst his blister;
And Charlotte says
that Robert kissed her:
He says he tried to
but he missed her.
And Miss, they're swinging
on the trees,
And Trevor Tonks
has cut his knees,
And Amy's found
a bunch of keys . . .

It's urgent!
Can you come, Miss, please?

Eric Finney

9

Conkers

This is a beauty,
brown and shiny.
The other conkers
all look tiny.

I thread the string
and then take aim.
I know I'm bound
to win the game.

I've had my go
and scored a hit.
Now Jenny tries
and misses it.

Another go.
I'm doing well.
Then Jenny's turn.
You just can't tell

Who's going to win.
She takes a hit.
Oh no! She's won!
My conker's split!

Jill Townsend

Playground quarrel

Yesterday at playtime
I quarrelled with my friend.
So she stopped playing,
And I stamped off saying,
'That's it then: that's the end!'

I've been sorry ever since:
She's kind and funny and clever.
That was yesterday.
We're friends today,
And we'll stay friends
For ever and ever.

Eric Finney

Inside, outside

When I'm sitting in class
I can't wait to get out,
To run and to chase
And to scramble about.

14

When I'm out in the cold
And the shivers begin
And the wind and the rain—
I can't wait to get in.

Richard James

15

On the slide

Fifteen steps
to the top of the slide.
I count them as I climb.

Whooosh!
I'm like a shooting star,
back down in record time!

Irene Rawnsley